MICHAEL ROSE

A Miscellany for Clarinet

BOOK I

THE ASSOCIATED BOARD OF
THE ROYAL SCHOOLS OF MUSIC

for Malcolm

A MISCELLANY FOR CLARINET
BOOK I

MICHAEL ROSE

Ballad

AB 2131

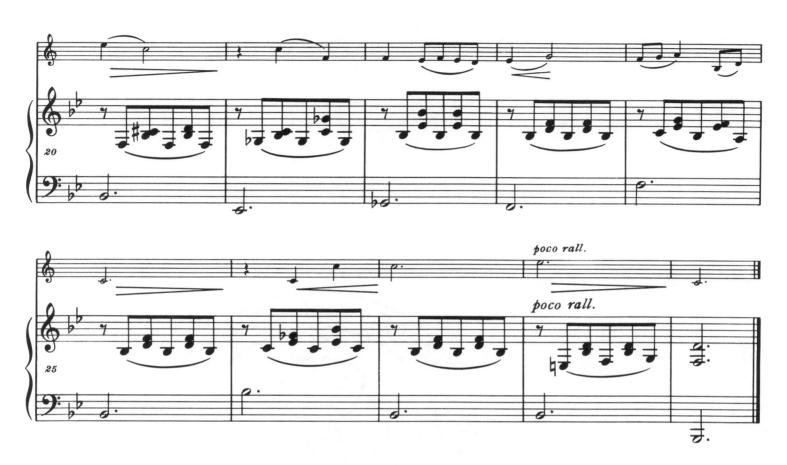

Valse

4

March

D.C. to $\bigoplus$ then to Coda

CODA

Serenade

Berceuse

Intermezzo

Allegro moderato-leggiero ♩.= 44-46

Barcarolle

4:04

for Malcolm

A MISCELLANY FOR CLARINET

BOOK I

CLARINET in B♭

MICHAEL ROSE

Ballad

Folksong

(unaccompanied)

AB 2131

Valse

Gavotte
(unaccompanied)

March

Serenade

Arietta
(unaccompanied)

Berceuse

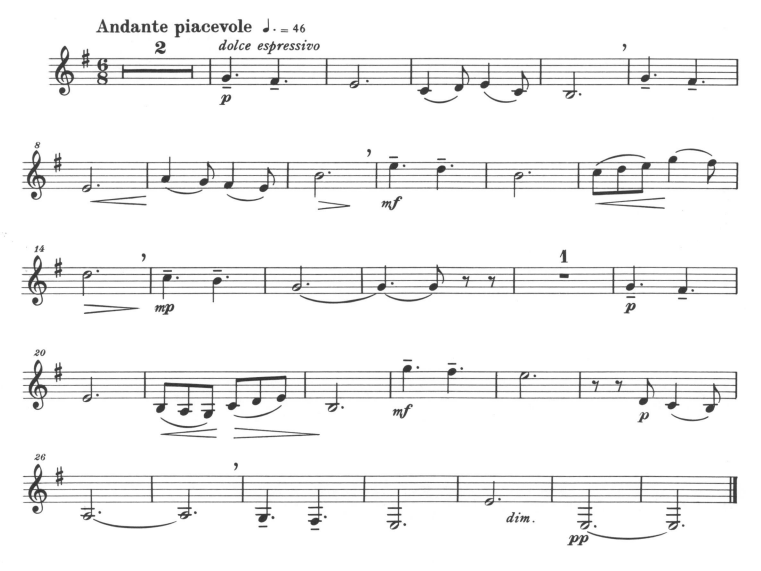

Intermezzo

Barcarolle

CLARINET in B♭

Aubade
(unaccompanied)

4:04